Emma

A graphic classic by
TRINA ROBBINS

Based on the novel by
JANE AUSTEN

SCHOLASTIC INC.
New York Toronto London Auckland Sydney
Mexico City New Delhi Hong Kong Buenos Aires

Penciller/Layouts
Jeff Warmeister

Colors, Inks, and Letters
Nimbus Studios

Cover Art
Phil Xavier and Nimbus Studios

Project Management
Greg Waller

5 6 7 8 9 10   23   10 09 08 07 06 05

Jane Austen

(1775–1817)

In Jane Austen's time, a young woman's most important job was to find a husband. So that's what Austen wrote about—young women and young men and the twists and turns of their romances.

Fortunately, those old ideas about women have become outdated. But Austen's stories haven't. In fact, a few years ago, the popular movie *Clueless* was based on Austen's *Emma*. In this novel, a young woman named Emma tries to fix up everyone around her—and she's totally clueless about what's best for them, and for herself.

Emma's World

Mr. Woodhouse
Emma's Father

George Knightley
Emma's friend

Emma Woodhouse

Jane Fairfax
Miss Bates's niece

Miss Bates
Emma's friend

Isabella Woodhouse Weston
Emma's sister

Mr. Weston
Isabella's husband

Harriet Smith
Emma's friend

Frank Weston
Mr. Weston's son

Robert Martin
Harriet's admirer

Mr. Elton
Emma's minister

Your poor sister! Now that she is married, she will live so far away from us. It is very unhealthy to walk such a distance.

Hush, Papa! Isabella is Mrs. Weston now, and when she wants to visit us, she can take the carriage.

But it will be lonely at home now.

6

Emma, I have good news! Robert Martin confided in me that he's very much in love with Harriet. He plans to ask her to marry him!

Mr. Martin has already proposed to Harriet, and she has refused him.

What a foolish girl! Emma, is this your doing?

Mr. Martin is only a farmer. He is Harriet's inferior.

What nonsense! Emma, I fear your friendship will not be good for Harriet.

14

23

DURING THE NEXT FEW MONTHS, EMMA AND FRANK SPEND A LOT OF TIME TOGETHER.

DRY GOODS

That sounds lovely.

Spring is here. Let's have a party at my father's house!

I hope she knows I just want to be friends.

I hope he knows I just want to be friends.

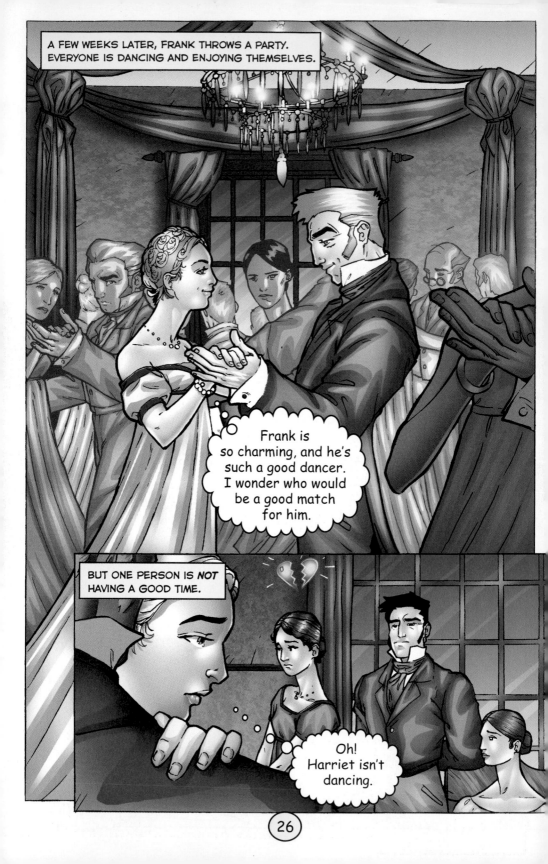

27

"SUDDENLY, I WAS APPROACHED BY TWO ROUGH-LOOKING STRANGERS. THEY ASKED FOR MONEY.

"ONE OF THEM TRIED TO TAKE MY PURSE.

"SUDDENLY, I HEARD THE SOUND OF HORSE'S HOOVES.

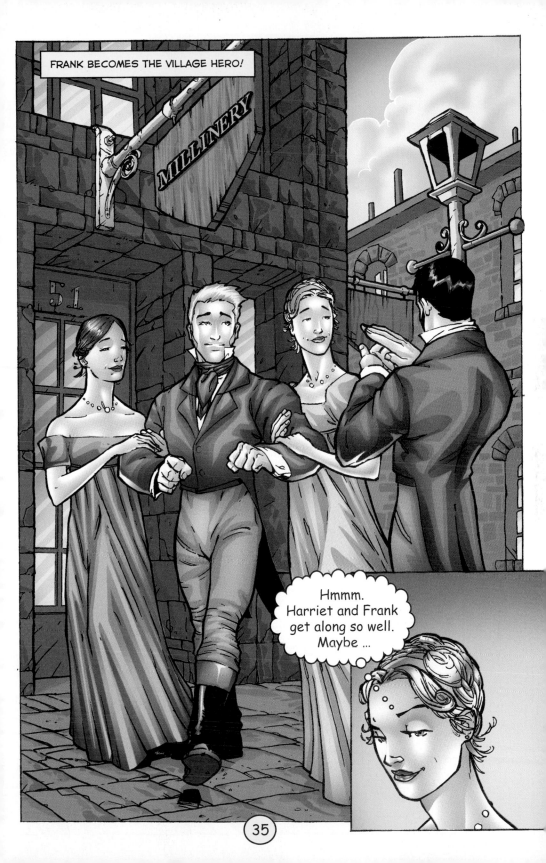

BEFORE THE END OF SEPTEMBER, EMMA GOES TO CHURCH FOR THE WEDDING OF HARRIET AND ROBERT MARTIN.

AND A FEW MOMENTS LATER, HARRIET AND ROBERT RETURN FOR THE WEDDING OF EMMA WOODHOUSE AND GEORGE KNIGHTLEY.

END